FLOW

OF

IONA

Jean M Millar

THE NEW IONA PRESS

First published by the Iona
Community, Glasgow, 1972.

Second edition published 1993 by
The New Iona Press Ltd.,
Old Printing Press Building,
Isle of Iona,
Argyll PA76 6SL.

ISBN   0 9516283 3 X

Printed in Britain by
Spectra Print, Glasgow.

---

*The publishers gratefully acknowledge financial assistance towards
the production of this publication from*
**The Glasgow Natural History Society
[the Professor Lloyd Binns Bequest Fund]**
and
Scottish Natural Heritage

**SCOTTISH
NATURAL
HERITAGE**

FOREWORD

Since my first edition of *Flowers of Iona* was published more than twenty years ago I have continued to visit the island at least four times a year, always looking at the native plants. In the first edition I list 200 species, whereas in this edition the number has more than doubled. This is not due to an increase in the flora, but is partly due to the fact that Rushes, Sedges, Grasses and Ferns have now been included and also because so many people have helped me over the years with new records.

In the introduction I point out that the ecology of Iona, as throughout much of the west coast of Scotland, may be changing due to alterations in farming methods. This may affect the flora of the island and so it is an important time to publish a complete list.

I thank all those who have helped me with records, and those who have provided information about farming and the ecology of Iona, especially Helen Rhodes, Keith Watson, Ken Tindall, Richard Leishman of Scottish Natural Heritage and Ross Lilley.

The main list gives for each species the botanical name, the common name and for the first time also the Gaelic name. These last were provided by Joan Clarke and I am very grateful to her for this most interesting addition and also for all her help with records. She has been for many years the County Recorder of The Botanical Society of the British Isles, for the area which includes Iona.

Lastly, I thank my publisher Mairi MacArthur. Her knowledge of the island and her enthusiasm for this present work has enabled me to bring it to completion. A flora is never entirely complete, however; there will be plants which have been overlooked or wrongly identified. I take responsibility for any mistakes and would be pleased to hear both about these and any new records.

Jean M. Millar
Spring 1993

Yellow Iris.

INTRODUCTION

Seen for the first time across the Sound from Fionnphort, Iona is strikingly different from Mull. The usual journey takes the traveller from the ferry terminal at Craignure through woods by Torosay, beside sea lochs and up over bleak Glen More. The road then follows Loch Scridain west along the Ross of Mull, dipping into Bunessan to rise again over moorland covered with outcrops of pink granite. Suddenly Iona is spread out across the Sound - seen immediately as a place of habitation with the Abbey, the village, the crofts and the arable fields. The destination is reached; there is nowhere farther to go.

The difference between the two islands is not imaginary. It is due to a variety of factors, many of which affect the flowers of Iona.

The geology of Mull and Iona is not the same. Central Mull is distinctive for the lava formations which flowed from huge volcanic activity about 60 million years ago. The red granite which was thrust upwards 400 million or so years ago, to form the area from Bunessan to Fionnphort, stretches underwater to several islets just off Iona's south-east coast but not to the island itself. Here, in contrast, is a layer of dark grey Torridonian flagstone along its eastern coast, deposited over the Lewisian gneiss which makes up the rest of Iona. At perhaps 2,800 million years old, this is among the most ancient exposed rock in Britain. The gneiss has weathered to a pale grey and in the higher parts of the island the soil in the hollows between the small hills is peaty and thin. Near the shore the soil is mixed with alkaline shell sand, supporting a flora quite distinct from the acidic bogs and heaths of the island's interior.

The climate of Iona is more like that of Coll and Tiree than Mull, with less rain and more sun. The moisture-laden south-west winds cross over these relatively low-lying islands before coming up against the higher hills of Mull and discharging their rain. Iona shares with the more westerly islands very strong winds, having little shelter and hardly any trees, although there would have been more shrubby woodland cover at one time. This level of exposure is such that a number of arctic alpine plants more typical of montane communities on higher ground are present, eg Roseroot. The whole west coast of Scotland is under the influence of the Gulf Stream which raises the temperature and prevents frost and snow in winter. These climatic differences mean that the midge population is much lower than on Mull - an important consideration for tourists.

Farming and Plant Life

Agriculture has been practised on Iona since the sixth century when Columba established a religious community here. It is likely that the island was already inhabited when he arrived in 563 AD but little is known about the way of life of the island people before that date. From Adomnan's *Life of Columba* we know that the monks grew crops and kept cattle and other stock. Since then the island has been under continuous cultivation and this has affected the composition of the flora. As well as the arable weeds which have become established, and the effect of grazing animals on pasture and hill-ground, there are the plants which were cultivated for food and medicine. Many of the arable weeds found here are becoming rare in other parts of Britain because of the intensive methods of farming on much of the mainland.

The future of agriculture on Iona depends on the grants and subsidies which will be on offer. At present grants are geared to the improvement of the quality rather than the quantity of stock. The Argyll islands were among new districts proposed as an 'Environmentally Sensitive Area' (ESA), whereby steps to enhance the environment receive specific funding, but it is not yet certain when this may come into practice. If it does, the effect on the flowers of Iona is not clear.

Recently much of the grass has been cut for silage, due to the fact that there is now a silage-baling machine on the island. For silage-making, grass is cut early before any arable weeds have had time to set seed. However, because the fields are small and often contain rocky outcrops which cannot be cultivated, there are many pockets where plants can come to maturity and are protected from grazing animals.

One farmer is still making hay and has taken part in an experimental scheme jointly funded by the Royal Society for the Protection of Birds and Scottish Natural Heritage to protect the habitat of the corncrake. These rare birds nest in hay fields, so the scheme demands that the hay is not cut until the chicks have hatched and then the mowing must start in the centre of the field and work outwards, allowing the chicks to escape. In 1992, although there was only one calling male, two broods were raised.

Both the silage and hay fields are sown with improved grass seed but because plenty of seed is produced in the pockets within the fields and at the field edges, it is unlikely that the arable weeds will die out.

There are two farms and fifteen crofts on the island, the rest of the land being divided into two common grazings for the two townships, or groups of holdings. The larger of these, the West End Common, includes the Machair and stretches south-west to the area around Loch Staonaig. The souming (recommended stocking level) for this Common is 220 sheep and 55 cows plus followers, but in fact the numbers are about 160 sheep and 25 cows. The sheep move to the high ground for part of the day but the quality, rather than the quantity, of the Machair grass attracts them back and the sheep grazing pressure here can be heavy. The cattle do a grand tour of the hill pasture and very often do not spend more than one day in seven on the Machair, when they will be on the shore-line eating the wrack. The smaller East End Common lies behind Dùn I and has a souming of 120 sheep and 24 cows. Again the actual numbers are lower, about 25 sheep and 12 cows.

On some Hebridean islands it was once usual not to graze machair in summer, a practice very favourable to the plants as it allowed them to flower and set seed. On Iona, by contrast, year-round grazing has been the norm for a long time.

Some hill areas become very rank and rough with old heather preventing new growth and when this happens, township members are permitted to burn the moorland at certain times of the year, taking into consideration the weather conditions and especially the wind direction.

The grazing pressures and this practice of moor burn affects the flora of the hill areas, as can be seen by comparing the vegetation in gullies and headlands inaccessible to stock. Several species are only found in such places and the vegetation is more luxuriant. Some very stunted trees - oak, aspen, hazel, willow and hawthorn - grow in the gullies of the south-east shore and it is probable that there was an area of scrubby woodland all along the hillside, sheltered from the prevailing wind, before man managed the land by increased grazing. Fencing to prevent access by stock, along with native tree planting, has been carried out on neighbouring Erraid where the trees are flourishing. It will be interesting to find out if this management alters the composition of the flora there.

Some of the Iona crofts have apportioned their share of the common grazing and these areas are adjacent to the crofts and fenced off. Because the areas are small and stocked only with sheep in order to be economically viable, they must be managed in a way which does not encourage the native flora.

The rabbit population, having been almost wiped out by myxamitosis, is on the increase again. These animals affect the plant populations in the same way as sheep and cattle but also, due to their burrowing habits, disturb the vegetation cover of the soil which allows erosion to start. On the sandy soils, favoured by rabbits, erosion can become a serious problem but it does allow for new plant populations to become established, as the bare soil encourages seed germination and growth. Common Stork's-bill is an example of a plant which thrives in such a situation.

At the North End there is the constant threat of erosion of the sand dunes by storms. Marram grass planting schemes have been sponsored by The National Trust for Scotland and Scottish Natural Heritage. Initially, six-foot high snow fences with vertical slats were erected. Then after two years, with very often only the top of the fence showing, the sand was stable enough for planting with marram. The area was then made stock-proof, which allowed the marram and other grasses to colonise the sand quickly. The crofter concerned is pleased with the scheme and considers it a success.

The ground around the village has been used for gardens for a long time and it is almost certain that both the Nunnery and the Abbey had gardens for medicinal and culinary herbs. The village is sheltered from the prevailing south-west winds and so here, due to the good soil and the skill of the gardeners, many attractive and colourful gardens have been established. As the street divides the houses from their front gardens, these give as much pleasure to passers-by as to the owners. Both the hotels run very successful vegetable gardens, the number of windbreaks erected around and within them showing clearly that the wind is the main problem of growing plants on the island.

The Impact of Visitors

Today Iona attracts a great many visitors. Day tourists arrive by the thousand during Summer, crossing Mull by bus and the Sound by the large ferry specially built for the route and launched in 1992. The Abbey caters for 100 visitors at a time, most of whom stay for a week, and this season lasts from March to October. The two hotels, various bed and breakfast places plus houses to let bring in a summer population several times larger than the number of residents, currently under 100.

It is not clear what effect this has on the ecology of the island or whether any plants have been introduced or lost to the flora from this cause. The National Trust for Scotland have helped visitors gain access to the North End and Dùn I by erecting stiles and gates but directing large numbers of people on one route can cause erosion, as can be seen on the path up Dùn I.

Many visitors enjoy the flowers of Iona, especially the colourful yellow irises in June and the beautiful orchids and other plants on the hill ground. Any future land management plan for the island must take note of this and also of the fact that change of land use will necessarily alter the composition of the flora. The National Trust for Scotland, owners of the island since 1979, and Scottish Natural Heritage are in favour of supporting traditional agricultural practices and hope that any decline in these will be stemmed, or even reversed, by the take-up of grants and subsidies such as may become available under ESA status.

The dilemma will be how to ensure a viable lifestyle for the resident population, while retaining the qualities of remoteness and beauty which draw visitors to the island.

Plant Recording on Iona

Iona is fortunate in having been visited by scholars over the years, attracted by the archaeology and geology. Many had a wide range of interests and made records of the plants they observed with the result that botanical records are available for the island as far back as the 18th century. Thomas Pennant, on his famous journey round the Hebrides in 1772, had with him the botanist Rev. John Lightfoot. In *Flora Scotica* he has several records from Y-Columb-Kill (Iona), mainly plants he would not have found elsewhere such as Wall Pennywort.

Sir Joseph Banks visited Iona and Staffa the same year, the only records from his visit being of Allseed, Isle of Man Cabbage, Butterbur and Marram Grass. The latter two records were recently found in an unpublished journal where he mentions the largest plants of Butterbur he had ever seen, growing in the churchyard. Their guide 'carried us under the ample shade of the Petasites (Butterbur), stopping here and there to inform us of the places where Kings and Nobles had been interred...'. He also writes that Marram Grass was used as winter feed for the black cattle on the island.

During the 19th century Iona was visited by many botanists, including William Hooker. Many first records from Iona and Staffa are to be found in the list published by W. Keddie, a lecturer in Natural Sciences at the Free Church College in Glasgow who was a regular visitor to the island. George Ross, one-time resident of Tobermory, also produced plant lists for Mull and Iona.

In 1978 the Department of Botany, British Museum (Natural History) published a comprehensive work entitled *The Island of Mull, a Survey of its Flora and Environment*. This was based on fieldwork carried out from 1966-1970 and includes all known records of plants found in written material and herbaria. Mull and the surrounding islands were divided into 17 sections, of which Iona was one on its own. The flora of any place is in constant state of change and the list I publish here is probably already out of date. Records are kept by the County Recorders of The Botanical Society of the British Isles and in 1990 an updating of records for this County was published in their journal *Watsonia*. Any new records should be sent to them.

How to Use this Guide

In the following pages I discuss the problems of flowering plants growing in four different habitats on Iona : the sandy shore, machair, hill (both heath and bog) and rock face. The illustrations show some of the plants typical of each habitat. I also illustrate some of the spring flowers as many of these have a special beauty.

I have not given times of flowering except for the early or late flowering species. Unless otherwise stated, the plants flower between mid-June and August. In order to help with identification I have also indicated whether the plant is 'frequent', 'occasional' or 'rare'.

The plants are listed in families following the names and order in *New Flora of the British Isles* (C.A. Stace, 1991) and *List of Vascular Plants of the British Isles* (D.H. Kent, 1992). The common names are from the same source, with a few local additions, and the Gaelic names have been added by Joan Clarke. The sedges, rushes, grasses and ferns follow the main plant list; they are not included in the alphabetical index.

Over the years there have been many introductions to the flora of Iona, either from agriculture or as garden escapes. These are included in the list if they survive outside the gardens and are reproducing by seed or in other ways.

A map on the last page shows the division between farmed and pasture land and the main place names mentioned in the text.

SPRING FLOWERS

Although the winters are windy, wet and dark, the temperature rarely stays below freezing for long, so ground frost is unusual and snow uncommon. This means that the spring flowers come into bloom as early and sometimes even earlier than on the mainland. The plants illustrated are in flower during April and May. They all store food in underground parts during the winter, which allows the plant to produce flowers as soon as there is sufficient light.

The Spring Squill has a bulb and after flowering the leaves die away, leaving only an inconspicuous dried-up stalk and seed head. The blue flowers are prolific by Sandeels Bay and come as a surprise to visitors who only know the island in summer. The Early Purple Orchid has underground tubers which take many years to develop before flowering occurs. It will only flower if conditions are favourable and some years there are no plants above ground.

Dog Violets and Primroses are very common on hill-ground and in gullies, where they are succeeded by Wild Hyacinths (English Bluebells) and Ramsons (Wild Garlic). Lesser Celandine is common in wet places across the island. It can easily be told from the buttercups, to which it is related, by its 8-10 petals and heart-shaped leaves.

The first plant to flower each spring is the Butterbur (not illustrated). These strange brush-like, lilac-pink flowers appear in early March before the leaves. The plants on Iona are all male and so seed is never produced. This means that the plants today have probably been reproduced vegetatively from the very plants seen by Joseph Banks in 1772. They are no longer in the graveyard but over the wall in the neighbouring fields. The plants were perhaps thrown there when the graveyard was tidied up earlier this century. The other place Butterbur grows well is by Martyrs Bay where the large, rhubarb-like leaves are noticeable all summer.

(Illustration opposite page 41)

SANDY SHORE

Sandy shores are not hospitable places for plants. The sand moves around, the winds are strong and salt-laden, the sunlight is fierce and fiercely reflected from the sand and there is a shortage of fresh water and humus. In spite of all this the beaches of Iona are colonised above the drift-line with great persistence by a variety of land plants.

One of the most striking and common of these is Silverweed. The name refers to the silver-backed leaves, the silky hairs which give this appearance reflecting light and heat away from the leaves, trapping moist, warm air and reducing water loss. Silverweed rapidly colonises the shore by sending out long, red, creeping stems which root at the nodes (like strawberry plants, which belong to the same family). If the parent plant is smothered by blown sand, any offshoots which remain uncovered can continue an independent existence.

Sea Rocket is an annual plant which is common some years at the North End and on Eilean Annraidh. It has not been found anywhere on Mull. The fruits of this plant can float and are unaffected by sea water, so it is surprising to find such a limited distribution. The plants manage to live in the sand by sending down a very long tap root which anchors it in the moving sand and reaches to any fresh water deep below the surface. This water can then be stored in the fleshy leaves.

Sea-holly was first recorded by Pennant in 1772 and then several times during the 19th century but it is now very rare. There is only one clump on the shore at the North End where it has been present for at least the last 20 years, looking very healthy some years with good strong side plants and many flowers. The plants may have died out completely by the beginning of this century and then been re-introduced in 1950.

One of the main ecological problems of any sandy shore area is the erosion and deposition due to strong winds. The sand can be fixed in dunes by various plants which are specially adapted for this function. In Iona Marram Grass is the most important dune-fixing plant. It cannot stand sea water but can become established above high-water mark and there the stiff leaves trap the blown sand. As the level of the sand builds up around the plants, new underground stems, known as rhizomes, are formed and eventually a huge underground network is built up. After the Marram Grass has become established other plants will come in and, as meadow land is formed, the Marram will die out. This is probably how the meadows at the North End and the Machair on the west shore were formed.

(Illustration opposite)

Plants of the Sandy Shore;
Ray's Knotgrass,   Sea-holly,
Silverweed,   Saltwort.

MACHAIR

Machair is the name given to the grassland lying behind the west shore of many Hebridean islands. It is often cultivated or used as common grazing, as on Iona. At first sight the vegetation seems to consist of only smooth, closely cropped grass but on closer examination many small flowering plants can be seen. These are often small specimens of plants which grow much larger in more sheltered, less grazed parts of the island.

The Wild Carrot (illustrated) shows the very short stem characteristic of the way they grow on the Machair, with the inflorescence often at ground level. Less than half a mile away this same species grows to a height of two to three feet at the edges of fields. If the seeds of the Machair plants are grown on, they always produce small plants whereas the field-edge plants always produce tall plants. This shows that the difference is genetic and that the Machair populations have evolved with a small form in order to be able to survive in this very windy, heavily grazed habitat. It is likely that many of the other Machair plants have similar variations and certainly it can be observed that the colours of the flowers are very intense.

Two of the plants illustrated take the names from the shape of the fruits. The Bird's-foot-trefoil fruit has very long pods which spread out to form a shape like a bird's foot. The individual fruits of Stork's-bill can be seen like the head of a stork, the remains of the style being the bill. When the fruit is ripe the style splits into five, from the base outwards, one seed being shot away from the parent plant from each part.

Wild Thyme covers large areas of the Machair and in July some of the slopes are purple with the flowers. The scent of the leaves is less strong than garden thyme but can be smelt when the leaves are crushed.

The flowers of Milkwort are usually deep blue but can also be purple, pink or white. The colour is in the two large inner sepals which enclose the rest of the flower. As the fruit develops the sepals turn green.

In the past the Machair was cultivated, potatoes and cereals being planted on ridges formed by bringing seaweed from the shore and heaping it up on top of the sandy soil. These ridges can still be seen, especially in low sunlight. Today much of the Machair is common grazing. It is of interest to compare the vegetation on the north side of the fence, an area farmed by Culbhuirg with a less heavy grazing regime. There are very many more flowering plants here and the individual plants are often larger than on the common grazing. The soil is rich on the Machair with nutrients from the drift of sea water, blown sand and seaweed, so grazing is good. On the common grazing there is an abundance of daisies and ribwort plantain, a sure indication of over-grazing.

The Machair has been used for many years as a natural golf course. The greens are kept short by the sheep so no grass-cutting is needed. It is unlikely that the playing of golf has had any effect on the vegetation.
(Illustration opposite page 36)

THE HILL

Ground on Iona which is neither inhabited nor arable is known in Gaelic as *an sliabh*, which means a tract of moorland, and is referred to locally as 'the hill'. It is divided in two by the strip of arable land which runs across the island from east to west at each side of the road to the Machair. Access to the southern area is by the track to Ruanaich or from the Machair to Loch Staonaig. The highest points of the south Hill are Druim Dhùghaill and at Càrn Cùl ri Eirinn. To the north the Hill lies west and south of Dùn I, Iona's highest point (332 feet), and is accessible by footpath from Achabhaich in the east or Port Bàn in the west.

The soil of the Hill is not very fertile, being acidic and shallow. Two main types of vegetation are found here, the heath plants in the drier areas and the bog plants in the wetter parts.

Heath Plants

Many heath plants are low, evergreen shrubs with small leaves and are adapted in various ways to withstand strong winds. Scottish Heather, or Ling, is common on Iona and is an important food source for sheep. It flowers in September, later than the two other heathers, Cross-leaved Heath and Bell Heather, which both flower in July and August. The flowers of Cross-leaved Heath are a delicate pale pink and this plant often grows in the wetter parts of the Hill, whereas Bell Heather has bright purplish-pink flowers which turn dull purple as they die and the plants are often found on cliff edges and rocky out-crops.

Juniper is found mainly on the south Hill. It suffers from the practice of heather burning and the dead silver-grey Juniper shoots can be seen amongst the renewed heather shoots in areas which have recently been burnt. The contortions of the branches can be traced along the ground, showing how this native shrub of Scotland adapts itself to a wind-swept habitat. It grows vigorously in areas which escape the fires, sometimes bearing the bitter, black, bloomed fruits

Heath Plants;
Heather, Cross-leaved Heath, Bell Heather,
Juniper, Crowberry, Creeping Willow.

which are used to flavour gin. The seedlings are often killed by grazing but once the plants are established would only be killed by very intense grazing.

Crowberry is a common, but undistinguished, plant growing on the drier parts of the Hill. The flowers appear in March and April, the male and female being on separate plants. The pollen is carried by the wind from the long purple stamens of the male to the short sticky stigmas of the female plants. It is rare to find the ripe black fruits, except on rocky islets or headlands inaccessible to sheep.

Creeping Willow is also common on high ground and like the Crowberry has male and female flowers on separate plants. Here the pollen is carried from the male to the female plants by insects which are attracted by nectar. In May the fruits, which are any colour from orange-red to green, burst open releasing the seeds, each with a parachute of silky hairs. In summer many of the Creeping Willow leaves have prominent orange-red galls. If these are cut open they will be seen to contain grubs of gall wasps.

(Illustration opposite page)

Bog Plants

Most bog plants are perennials, the leaves and flowers dying down in winter and growing again the following spring. They differ from the heath plants in having large leaves and brightly coloured flowers.

The roots of bog plants are submerged in stagnant water for much of the year so, in order to ensure an adequate oxygen supply, there are special air channels within the roots. Because the soil is waterlogged, and there is little through-flow, the lack of oxygen does not allow for many bacteria capable of breaking down organic matter for the release of nitrogenous compounds. Insectiverous plants demonstrate a strange way of obtaining these. They trap insects and then kill them in order to extract nitrogen from their decaying bodies

There are three different sorts of insectiverous plants on Iona. The Butterworts, both the early Common Butterwort with large bright yellow leaves and the later Pale Butterwort with small sickly yellow leaves, produce a sticky substance on the surface of the leaves which traps insects. All three species of Sundew have rosettes of leaves which are covered with hairs. These hairs have globular ends and when an insect falls on the leaf the hairs curl over to trap it and remain in this position until the insect dies. Bladderwort grows in some of the peaty pools. It is a very small plant and needs to be magnified to show the bladders on the stems. These bladders have trap-doors which open when triggered by moving water organisms. As the trap-door opens, water flows into the bladder taking the organism with it.

Many Orchids obtain nutrients by having fungi associated with their root systems, which are capable of breaking down plant remains in the soil. This is the method used by the Heath Spotted Orchid which grows in such profusion on the island.

Lousewort and its near relative Red Rattle obtain extra nutrients by being semi-parasitic on the neighbouring grasses.

Marsh St. John's-wort looks unlike other members of this distinctive family because the leaves are covered with white hairs. These hairs trap air, permitting oxygen to reach the leaf surface when the water level is high. One of the smallest bog plants is Bog Pimpernel, which often goes unnoticed as the pale pink flowers shut in dull weather. The small umbrella-shaped leaves of Marsh Pennywort are often seen in the bogs but their tiny green flowers are hard to find.

(Illustration opposite page 32)

ROCK FACE

Some flowers grow from what seems to be bare rock but, unless it has recently split open, rock is rarely completely bare from a botanical point of view. Lichens and mosses quickly colonise rock faces, eating into the surface and allowing soil to build up in cracks and crevices. Seeds of higher plants germinate in this soil but only those plants specially adapted to this habitat will survive. All such plants have strong, long root systems which travel far into the rock crevices. This in turn further splits the rock, allowing more soil to accumulate. Some of these plants also have fleshy leaves, which can store water during dry periods.

Roseroot is a good example of a plant with fleshy leaves and a large root system. The male and female flowers are on separate plants which, early in summer, look the same. However, it is only the female plants which have the colourful orange-red fruits which persist for a long time after the flowers. The name comes from the fact that the dying root is said to smell of roses.

Thrift, as well as being able to grow on rock faces, can also withstand salt and so grows far down on the rocky shore. It has a very large and tough root system but the leaves are narrow and curled lengthwise to prevent evaporation of water rather than being fleshy to store water. The leaves form a cushion, which provides less surface area for water evaporation and also creates a microclimate of warmer air, allowing the plant to flower early in the season.

Navelwort or Wall Pennywort has a curious appearance, with tall spikes of yellowish-green flowers and round fleshy leaves. The leaves give rise to both its common names, the shape of the leaves being like a penny and the dimple in the centre like a navel. Although fairly common on Iona, it is rare on Mull. Navelwort is a Mediterranean plant, growing through the winter and then dying away after flowering to avoid the arid conditions which can be experienced on rock faces during summer months.

Bloody Cranesbill is one of the most striking plants of Iona and, although common on the nearby small islands, it is very uncommon on Mull.

Red Valerian is a plant of the rock face but is not indigenous to Iona. Many years ago a packet of seed was sown in the Nunnery garden and all the plants there come from this source. It has now become a weed and, because its roots can destroy the ancient walls, it has to be destroyed. Ivy leaved Toodflax was introduced to the Nunnery at the same time and has spread with equal success, but as it is harmless to the walls it has been allowed to stay.

(Illustration overleaf)

Plants of the Rock face;
Wall Pennywort, Bloody Crane's-bill, Rose-root,
Thrift.

THE FLOWERING PLANTS OF IONA
arranged in their Botanical Families

★ indicates a reference in the text
+ indicates an illustration

CUPRESSACEAE
1   **★+ Juniperus communis subsp alpina** Juniper *Iubhar Beinne*
     Frequent on dry parts of hill.
NYMPHAEACEAE
2   **Nymphaea alba** White Water-lily *Duilleag-Bhàite Bhàn*
     In Loch Staonaig before enlargement as reservoir; not found since.
RANUNCULACEAE
3   **Caltha palustris** Marsh-marigold *Lus Buidhe Bealltainn*
     Early flowering, frequent in wet areas.
4   **Anemone nemorosa** Wood Anemone *Flùr na Gaoithe*
     Early flowering in damp gullies.
5   **Ranunculus acris** Meadow Buttercup *Buidheag an t-Samhraidh*
     Frequent in arable fields etc.
6   **Ranunculus repens** Creeping Buttercup *Buidheag*
     Frequent in waste areas and as a garden weed.
7   **Ranunculus bulbosus** Bulbous Buttercup *Fuile-thalmhainn*
     Frequent in sandy areas, distinguished from other buttercups by
     reflexed sepals.
8   **Ranunculus flammula** Lesser Spearwort *Glaisleun*
     Frequent in wet areas; flowers similar to buttercups but leaves spearlike.
9   **★+ Ranunculus ficaria** Lesser Celandine *Searragaich/Gràn Aigein*
     Early flowering; frequent.
10   **Ranunculus hederaceus** Ivy-leaved Crowfoot *Fleann Uisge Eidheannach*
     Occasional on wet mud; small white flowers.
11   **Thalictrum minus subsp. arenarium** Lesser Meadow-rue *Rù Beag*
     Occasional on sandy soil by rocky outcrops, or on walls; recorded by Lightfoot
     from Iona 1772.
PAPAVERACEAE
12   **Papaver somniferum** Opium Poppy *Lus a' Chadail*
     Garden escape, near village.
13   **Papaver rhoeas** Common Poppy *Meilbheag*
     Rare arable weed.
14   **Papaver dubium** Long-headed Poppy *Crom-lus Fad-cheannach*
     Arable weed, more common than above species.

FUMARIACEAE

15   **Fumaria bastardii** Tall Ramping-fumitory *Fuaim an t-Siorraimh*
Arable weed.

16   **Fumaria muralis** Common Ramping-fumitory *Dearag Thalmhainn*
Arable weed.

17   **Fumaria officinalis** Common fumitory *Lus Deathach-thalmhainn*
Arable weed.

ULMACEAE

18   **Ulmus glabra** Wych Elm *Leamhan*
In village, probably planted.

URTICACEAE

19   **Urtica dioica** Common Nettle *Deanntag/Feanntag*
Frequent in waste places, especially beside farm buildings.

20   **Urtica urens** Annual Nettle *Deanntag Bhliadhnail*
Rare arable weed.

MYRICACEAE

21   **Myrica gale** Bog-myrtle *Roid*
Occasional in wet areas on hill.

FAGACEAE

22   **Quercus Robur** Pedunculate Oak *Darach*
Very stunted but probably old trees growing in cliffs on SE coast; acorns never
found.

BETULACEAE

23   **Betula pubescens** Downy Birch *Beith Charraigeach*
Shrubby plants in gullies on hill.

24   **Alnus glutinosa** Alder *Feàrna*
Introduced species.

25   **Corylus avellana** Hazel *Calltainn*
Found with birch and oak in gullies.

CHENOPODIACEAE

26   **Chenopodium bonus–henricus** Good-King-Henry *Praiseach-bràthar*
Rare waste ground weed.

27   **Chenopodium album** Fat-hen *Càl Liath-ghlas* (Argyll)
Rare waste ground weed.

28   **Atriplex glabriuscula** Babington's Orach *Praiseach Mhìn Chladaich*
On beaches above drift line.

29   **Atriplex patula** Common Orach *Praiseach Mhìn Chaol*
Rare.

30   **Beta vulgaris subsp. maritima** Sea Beet *Biatas Mara*
Rare, on beach above drift line.

31   **+ Salsola kali** Prickly Saltwort *Lus an t-Salainn*
Common on E shore, above drift line.

PORTULACACEAE
32　**Montia fontana** Blinks *Fliodh Uisge*
Very small plant, on wet tracks on hill.

CARYOPHYLLACEAE
33　**Arenaria serpyllifolia** Thyme-leaved sandwort *Lus nan Naoi Alt*
Rare, on sand at coast.

34　**Honckenya peploides** Sea Sandwort *Lus a' Ghoill*
On shore above drift line.

35　**Stellaria media** Common Chickweed *Fliodh*
Frequent weed of waste ground.

36　**Stellaria uliginosa** Bog Stitchwort *Flige*
In marshy areas.

37　**Cerastium tomentosum** Snow-in-summer *Cluas Luch Ghàrraidh*
Garden escape.

38　**Cerastium fontanum subsp. trivale** Common Mouse-ear
Cluas Luch
Frequent on waste ground and sandy shore.

39　**Cerastium glomeratum** Sticky Mouse-ear *Cluas Luch Fhàireagach*
As above species but less common.

40　**Cerastium diffusum** Sea Mouse-ear *Cluas Luch Mara*
Frequent on Machair and in rock crevices.

41　**Cerastium semidecandrum** Little Mouse-ear *Cluas Luch Bheag*
As above species but much less common.

42　**+ Sagina nodosa** Knotted Pearlwort *Mungan Snaimte*
Frequent on Machair.

43　**Sagina subulata** Heath Pearlwort *Mungan Mòintich*

44　**Sagina procumbens** Procumbent Pearlwort *Mungan Làir*

45　**Sagina apetala** Annual Pearlwort *Mungan Bliadhnail*
Rare.

46　**Sagina maritima** Sea Pearlwort *Mungan Mara*
Rare.

47　**Spergula arvensis** Corn Spurrey *Cluain-lìn / Corran-lìn*
Arable weed.

48　**Lychnis flos-cuculi** Ragged Robin *Sìoda-lus / Caorag Lèana*
Occasional in damp fields.

49　**Agrostemma githago** Corn-cockle *Lus Loibheach*
Rare arable weed.

50　**Silene uniflora** Sea Campion *Coirean na Mara*
Frequent on coast amongst rocks and on cliffs.

51　**Silene latifolia** White Campion *Coirean Bàn*
Rare.

52　**Silene dioica** Red Campion *Cìrean Coilich*
Occasional in gullies.

POLYGONACEAE

53   **Persicaria amphibia** Amphibious Bistort *Glùineach an Uisge*
By streams and in wet areas.

54   **Persicaria maculosa** Redshank *Glùineach Dhearg*
Arable weed.

55   **Persicaria lapathifolia** Pale Persicaria *Glùineach Bhàn*
Rare.

56   **Persicaria hydropiper** Water-pepper *Glùineach Theth / Piobar Uisge*
Occasional in marshy fields.

57   **+ Polygonum oxyspermum** Ray's Knotgrass *Glùineach na Tràighe*
On sandy shore above drift line, E coast.

58   **Polygonum aviculare** Knotgrass *Glùineach Bheag*
Occasional on waste ground.

59   **Fallopia convolvulus** Black Bindweed *Glùineach Dhubh*
Rare arable weed.

60   **Rumex acetosella** Sheep's Sorrel *Sealbhag nan Caorach*
Frequent on hill.

61   **Rumex acetosa** Common Sorrel *Sealbhag / Samh*
Frequent on pasture and by seabird nest sites.

62   **Rumex crispus** Curled Dock *Copag Chamagach*
Frequent in waste places and amongst rocks on shore.

63   **Rumex conglomeratus** Clustered Dock *Copag Bhagaideach*
Rare.

64   **Rumex sanguineus var.viridus** Wood Dock *Copag Choille*
Rare.

65   **Rumex obtusifolius** Broad-leaved Dock *Copag Leathann*
Frequent as arable weed and on waste ground.

PLUMBAGINACEAE

66   ***+ Armeria maritima** Thrift *Neòinean Cladaich*
Frequent on all coasts.

CLUSIACEA [Hypericaceae]

67   **Hypericum calycinum** Rose-of-Sharon *Seud Chaluim Chille*
Garden escape.

68   **Hypericum androsaemum** Tutsan *Meas an Tuirc Coille*
Occasional in gullies.

69   **Hypericum tetrapterum** Square-stalked St John's-wort
Beachnuadh Fireann
Occasional in damp areas.

70   **Hypericum pulchrum** Slender St John's-wort *Lus Chaluim Chille*
Frequent on dry banks.

71   ***+ Hypericum elodes** Marsh St John's-wort *Meas an Tuirc-Allta*
Occasional in bogs on hill; rare on Mull.

MALVACEAE

72 **Malva sylvestris** Common Mallow *Lus nam Meall Mòra*
Rare; on waste ground.

DROSERACEAE

73 **★+ Drosera rotundifolia** Round-leaved Sundew *Lus na Feàrnaich*
Frequent in bogs.

74 **Drosera longifolia** Great Sundew *Lus a' Ghadmainn*
Rare.

75 **Drosera intermedia** Oblong-leaved Sundew *Dealt Ruaidhe*
Rare.

VIOLACEAE

76 **★+ Viola riviniana** Common Dog-violet *Dail-chuach*
Early flowering, often found with primroses on slopes of hill.

77 **Viola palustris** Marsh Violet *Dail-chuach Lèana*
Later flowering than above species, frequent in bogs.

78 **Viola tricolor subsp. curtisii** Wild Pansy
Goirmean-searradh nan Coilleag
Rare on sand dunes and Machair.

79 **Viola arvensis** Field Pansy *Luibh Chridhe*
Rare arable weed.

SALICACEAE

80 **Populus tremula** Aspen *Critheann*
In E coast gullies with oak, never seen in fruit.

81 **Salix caprea** Goat Willow *Suileag / Geal-sheileach*

82 **Salix aurita** Eared Willow *Seileach Cluasach*

83 **★+ Salix repens** Creeping Willow *Seileach Làir*
Frequent on hill with heather. Subsp. argentea has been recorded.

BRASSICACEAE [Cruciferae]

84 **Sisymbrium officinale** Hedge Mustard *Meilise*
Rare waste ground weed.

85 **Hesperis matronalis** Dame's-violet *Feasgar-lus*
Rare; in field margin.

86 **Rorippa nasturtium–aquaticum** Water-cress *Biolair*
Occasional in burns.

87 **Rorippa microphylla** Narrow-fruited Water-cress *Mion-bhiolair*
Less common than above species.

88 **Cardamine pratensis** Cuckoo-flower *Flùr na Cuthaig*
Frequent in damp fields.

89 **Cardamine flexuosa** Wavy Bitter-cress *Searbh-bhiolair Chasta*
Frequent in damp shady places.

90 **Cardamine hirsuta** Hairy Bitter-cress *Searbh-bhiolair Ghiobach*
Less common than above species, in drier places.

91 **Arabis hirsuta** Hairy Rock-cress *Biolair na Creige Ghiobach*
Rare, on roadsides and rocky places.

92   **Draba incana**   Hoary Whitlow-grass   *Biolradh Gruagain Liath*
Rare, on Machair, no recent records.

93   **Erophila verna**   Common Whitlow-grass   *Biolradh Gruagain*
Rare.

94   **Cochlearia officinalis subsp. officinalis**   Common Scurvy-grass
Am Maraiche / Carran
In cave entrances, large leaved and luxuriant near bird colonies.

95   **Cochlearia officinalis subsp. scotica**   Scottish Scurvy-grass
Carran Albannach
On shore rocks, probably most common species on E coast.

96   **Cochlearia danica**   Danish Scurvy-grass   *Carran Danmhairceach*
As above species, but on W coast.

97   **Capsella bursa-pastoris**   Shepherd's-purse   *An Sporan / Lus na Fala*
Weed of arable and waste ground.

98   **Coronopus squamatus**   Swine-cress   *Muic-bhiolair*
Rare.

99   **Coronopus didymus**   Lesser Swine-cress   *Muic-bhiolair as Lugha*
Recorded by Ewing, 1880 but not since.

100   **Brassica napus**   Rape   *Raib / Snèap Suaineach*
Rare weed of arable and waste ground.

101   **Sinapis arvensis**   Charlock   *Sgeallan*
Rare weed of arable and waste ground.

102   ⋆ **Coincya monensis**   Isle of Man Cabbage
Specimen collected by Banks 1772 in British Museum Herbarium; not recorded since.

103   ⋆ **Cakile maritima**   Sea Rocket   *Fearsaideag*
At North End and Eilean Annraidh, not found on Mull.

104   **Raphanus raphanistrum**   Wild Radish   *Meacan Ruadh Fiadhain*
Rare weed of arable and waste ground.

EMPETRACEAE

105   ⋆+ **Empetrum nigrum**   Crowberry   *Lus na Feannaig*
Frequent on drier parts of the hill, flowers inconspicuous, April–May, fruits seldom seen.

ERICACEAE

106   ⋆+ **Calluna vulgaris**   Heather   *Fraoch*
Frequent on hill.

107   ⋆+ **Erica tetralix**   Cross-leaved Heath   *Fraoch Frangach*
Frequent in bogs.

108   ⋆+ **Erica cinerea**   Bell Heather   *Fraoch a' Bhadain / Biadh na Circe-fraoich*
Frequent on cliff ledges and drier parts of the hill.

109   **Vaccinium myrtillus**   Blaeberry   *Caora-mhitheag*
Frequent on hill.

PRIMULACEAE

110 **⋆+ Primula vulgaris** Primrose *Sòbhrach*
Frequent in gullies and clefts on hill, early flowering.

111 **Lysimachia nemorum** Yellow Pimpernel *Seamrag Moire*
Occasional in wet areas.

112 **⋆+ Anagallis tenella** Bog Pimpernel *Falcair Lèana*
Frequent in bogs.

113 **Anagallis arvensis** Scarlet Pimpernel *Falcair*
Occasional arable weed.

114 **Anagallis minima** Chaffweed *Falcair Mìn*
Rare.

115 **Glaux maritima** Sea Milk-wort *Lus na Saillteachd*
Frequent in sandy turf above shore.

116 **Samolus valerandi** Brookweed *Luibh an t-Sruthain*
Occasional in burns.

CRASSULACEAE

117 **⋆+ Umbilicus rupestris** Navelwort or Wall Pennywort *Leacan*
Occasional on sheltered cliffs, more common here than on Mull.
Recorded by Lightfoot, 1772.

118 **⋆+ Sedum rosea** Roseroot *Lus nan Laoch*
Frequent on cliffs.

119 **Sedum acre** Biting Stonecrop *Grabhan nan Clach*
Occasional on sand or walls.

120 **Sedum anglicum** English Stonecrop *Biadh an t-Sionnaidh*
Frequent on rocks and cliffs.

SAXIFRAGACEAE

121 **Saxifraga tridactylites** Rue-leaved Saxifrage
Clach-bhrìseach na Machrach
Rare.

122 **Chrysosplenium oppositifolium** Opposite-leaved Golden-saxifrage
Lus nan Laogh
Occasional, early flowering, in damp shady places.

123 **Parnassia palustris** Grass-of-Parnassus *Fionn-sgoth*
Rare on Iona, much more frequent on Erraid.

ROSACEAE

124 **Filipendula ulmaria** Meadowsweet *Cneas Chù Chulainn*
Frequent in ditches.

125 **Rubus saxatilis** Stone Bramble *Caor Bad Miann*
Occasional.

126 **Rubus idaeus** Raspberry *Subh-craoibh*
Garden escape.

127 **Rubus fruticosus agg.** Bramble *Dris* (bush) / *Smeur* (berry)
Frequent.

128 **Potentilla palustris** Marsh Cinquefoil *Còig-bhileach Uisge*
Frequent in bogs.

129 ***+ Potentilla anserina** Silverweed *Brisgean*
Frequent on the shore and as a weed of waste places.

130 **Potentilla erecta** Tormentil *Cairt Làir*
Abundant everywhere on the hill.

131 **Fragaria vesca** Wild Strawberry *Subh-làir Brèige*
Rare, only one record.

132 **Geum rivale** Water Avens *Machall Uisge*
Occasional in wet places.

133 **Geum urbanum** Wood Avens *Machall Coille*
Rare.

134 **Alchemilla glabra** Lady's-mantle *Fallaing Moire*
Frequent.

135 **Aphanes inexspectata** Parsley-piert *Spìonan Moire Caol*
Arable weed.

136 **Rosa pimpinellifolia** Burnet Rose *Ròs Beag Bàn na h-Alba*
Occasional on cliffs.

137 **Rosa canina group** Dog Rose *Ròs nan Con*
Occasional in gullies.

138 **Prunus spinosa** Blackthorn or Sloe *Sgitheach Dubh/Preas nan Airneag*
Rare.

139 **Malus sylvestris** Crab Apple *Goirteag*
Only one plant found, at Dun Bhuirg.

140 **Sorbus aucuparia** Rowan *Caorann*
Frequent in gullies.

141 **Sorbus intermedia** Swedish White-beam *Gall-uinnseann Suaineach*
Introduced tree.

142 **Cotoneaster integrifolius** Small-leaved Cotoneaster
Cotaineastar Mion-dhuilleagach
Rare; on cliff face.

143 **Crataegus monogyna** Hawthorn *Sgitheach*
Occasional.

FABACEAE [Leguminosae]

144 **Anthyllis vulneraria** Kidney-vetch *Cas an Uain*
Occasional on cliff edges.

145 ***+ Lotus corniculatus** Common Bird's-foot-trefoil
Barra-mhìslean/Peasair a' Mhadaidh-ruaidh
Frequent and widespread.

146 **Vicia cracca** Tufted Vetch *Peasair nan Luch*
Occasional in field edges.

147 **Vicia hirsuta** Hairy Tare *Peasair an Arbhair*
Rare, on waste ground.

148 **Vicia sepium** Bush Vetch *Peasair nam Preas*
Occasional on roadsides.
149 **Vicia sativa** Common Vetch *Peasair Chapaill*
Occasional.
150 **Lathyrus linifolius** Bitter-vetch *Cairt Leamhna*
Frequent.
151 **Lathyrus pratensis** Meadow Vetchling *Peasair Bhuidhe*
Occasional.
152 **Trifolium repens** White Clover *Seamrag Bhàn*
Frequent, often sown to improve pasture.
153 **Trifolium campestre** Hop Trefoil *Seamrag Bhuidhe*
Rare, near E shore.
154 **Trifolium dubium** Lesser Trefoil *Seangan*
More frequent than above species.
155 **Trifolium pratense** Red Clover *Seamrag Dhearg*
Frequent, probably much introduced as T. repens.
156 **Trifolium medium** Zigzag Clover *Seamrag Chrò-dhearg*
Rare.

HALORAGACEAE
157 **Myriophyllum alterniflorum** Alternate Water-milfoil
Snàthainn Bhàthaidh
In peaty pools.

LYTHRACEAE
158 **Lythrum salicaria** Purple Loosestrife *Lus na Sìochaint*
Occasional in ditches.
159 **Lythrum portula** Water-purslane *Flùr Bogaich Ealaidheach*
Rare, not found in Mull.

ONAGRACEAE
160 **Epilobium parviflorum** Hoary Willowherb *Seileachan Liath*
Rare, in ditches.
161 **Epilobium montanum** Broad-leaved Willowherb *Seileachan Coitcheann*
Frequent and widespread.
162 **Epilobium obscurum** Short-fruited Willowherb *Seileachan Fàireagach*
Occasional.
163 **Epilobium palustre** Marsh Willowherb *Seileachan Lèana*
Frequent in ditches.
164 **Chamerion angustifolium** Rosebay Willowherb *Seileachan Frangach*
Occasional on waste ground.
165 **Fuchsia magellanica** Fuchsia *Fiuise*
Garden escape.

EUPHORBIACEAE
166 **Mercurialis perennis** Dog's Mercury *Lus-ghlinne*
Occasional in gullies.

167 Euphorbia helioscopia Sun Spurge *Lus nam Foinneachan*
Rare arable weed.

168 Euphorbia peplus Petty Spurge *Lus Leighis*
Rare, on roadside, not found on Mull.

LINACEAE

169 Linum catharticum Fairy Flax *Lìon nam Ban-sìdh*
Occasional on dry grassy slopes.

170 ★ Radiola linoides Allseed *Lus Meanbh Meanganach*
Rare, on sandy ground; recorded by Banks 1772.

POLYGALACEAE

171 ★+ Polygala vulgaris Common Milkwort *Lus a' Bhainne*
Frequent on Machair.

172 Polygala serpyllifolia Heath Milkwort *Siabann nam Ban-sìdh*
Prefers more acid soil than above species.

ACERACEAE

173 Acer pseudoplatanus Sycamore *Craobh Pleantrainn*
The most common tree to obtain any height on Iona but even this tough
species has problems with the wind.

OXALIDACEAE

174 Oxalis acetosella Wood Sorrell *Feada-coille/Biadh nan Eòinean*
Early flowering in sheltered gullies.

GERANIACEAE

175 Geranium pratense Meadow Cranesbill *Crobh Preachain an Lòin*
Garden escape.

176 ★+ Geranium sanguineum Bloody Crane's-bill *Creachlach Dearg*
Frequent on cliffs; recorded by Lightfoot 1772.

177 Geranium dissectum Cut-leaved Crane's-bill *Crobh Preachain Gèarrte*
Rare, in centre of island.

178 Geranium molle Dovesfoot Crane's-bill *Crobh Preachain Mìn*
Frequent on Machair.

179 Geranium robertianum Herb Robert *Lus an Ròis/Ruideal*
Frequent in gullies.

180 ★+ Erodium cicutarium Common Stork's-bill *Gob Corra*
Frequent on Machair.

ARALIACEAE

181 Hedera helix Ivy *Eidheann*
Frequent on sheltered cliff faces.

APIACEAE

182 ★ Hydrocotyle vulgaris Marsh Pennywort *Lus na Peighinn*
Frequent in bogs.

183 ★+ Eryngium maritimum Sea-holly *Cuileann Tràgha*
Rare, at top of sandy beach above drift line. Recorded by Pennant 1772 and as
frequent by Keddie 1850; now only one locality.

184 **Anthriscus sylvestris** Cow Parsley *Costag Fhiadhain*
Occasional, usually by buildings.

185 **Conopodium majus** Pignut *Cnò-thalmhainn*
With bracken on hill.

186 **Pimpinella saxifraga** Lesser Burnet-saxifrage *Ainis Fhiadhain*
Occasional in areas with shell sand, usually on grassy slopes.

187 **Aegopodium podagraria** Ground-elder *Lus an Easbaig*
Garden and arable weed.

188 **Oenanthe crocata** Hemlock Water-dropwort *Dàtha Bàn Iteodha*
Rare, in ditches on Machair.

189 **Conium maculatum** Hemlock *Iteodha*
Rare garden weed.

190 **Apium inundatum** Lesser Marshwort *Fualactar*
At Loch Staonaig, not on Mull.

191 **Ligusticum scoticum** Scots Lovage *Sunais*
Frequent on rocks and cliffs of W coast, recorded by Lightfoot 1772.

192 **Angelica sylvestris** Wild Angelica *Lus nam Buadh/Aingealag*
Frequent in ditches.

193 **Heracleum sphondylium** Hogweed *Odharan*
Frequent in ditches.

194 **★+ Daucus carota subsp. carota** Wild Carrot *Curran Talmhainn*
Frequent on sandy soil.

GENTIANACEAE

195 **Centaurium erythraea** Common Centaury *Ceud-bhileach/Deagha Dearg*
Frequent in short sandy grass by sea on W coast.

196 **Gentianella campestris** Field Gentian *Lus a' Chrubain*
Occasional on ledges, with sandy soil.

SOLANACEAE

197 **Lycium barbarum** Duke of Argyll's Tea-plant *Preas Mhic Cailein Mhòir*
Garden escape, growing in walls.

CONVOLVLACEAE

198 **Convolvulus arvensis** Field Bindweed *Adh-lus*
Rare arable and garden weed.

199 **Calystegia sepium** Hedge Bindweed *Duil Mhial*
Rare garden weed.

200 **Calystegia pulchra** Hairy Bindweed *Duil Mhial Ghiobach*
Rare garden weed.

201 **Calystegia silvatica** Large Bindweed *Duil Mhial Mhòr*
Rare garden weed.

MENYANTHACEAE

202 **Menyanthes trifoliata** Bogbean *Trì-bhileach/Pònair Chapaill*
Occasional in peaty pools.

BORAGINACEAE

203 **Symphytum x uplandicum** Russian Comfrey *Meacan Dubh Ruiseanach*
Rare, near houses.

204 **Anchusa arvensis** Bugloss *Lus Teanga an Daimh*
Rare, arable weed.

205 **Pentaglottis sempervirens** Green Alkanet *Bog-lus*
Rare, near houses.

206 **Borago officinalis** Borage *Barraisd*
Garden escape.

207 **Mertensia maritima** Oysterplant *Tiodhlac na Mara*
Historical record, Pennant 1772. BM found only one stunted plant. Could return, large colony exists on Treshnish Islands.

208 **Myosotis scorpioides** Water Forget-me-not *Cotharach*
Frequent in burns and wet places.

209 **Myosotis secunda** Creeping Forget-me-not *Lus Midhe Ealaidheach*
Frequent in wet places.

210 **Myosotis laxa ssp. cespitosa** Tufted Forget-me-not
Lus Midhe Dosach
Occasional in wet places.

211 **Myosotis arvensis** Field Forget-me-not *Lus Midhe Aitich*
Occasional on waste ground and Machair.

212 **Myosotis discolor** Changing Forget-me-not
Lus Midhe Caochlaideach
Occasional.

LAMIACEAE [Labiatae]

213 **Stachys sylvatica** Hedge Woundwort *Lus nan Sgor*
Occasional.

214 **Stachys palustris** Marsh Woundwort *Brisgean nan Caorach*
Occasional in damp places.

215 **Stachys arvensis** Field Woundwort *Creuchd-lus Arbhair*
Rare.

216 **Lamium purpureum** Red Dead-nettle *Deanntag Dhearg*
Arable and garden weed.

217 **Lamium hybridum** Cut-leaved Dead-nettle *Deanntag Gheàrrte*
Arable weed.

218 **Lamium confertum** Northern Dead-nettle *Deanntag Thuathach*
Occasional arable and garden weed.

219 **Lamium amplexicaule** Henbit Dead-nettle *Deanntag Chearc*
Occasional arable and garden weed.

220 **Galeopsis tetrahit** Common Hemp-nettle *Deanntag Lìn/Gath Dubh*
Occasional arable weed.

221 **Galeopsis speciosa** Large-flowered Hemp-nettle *An Gath Mòr*
Rare arable weed.

Bog Plants;
Common Butterwort, Lousewort, Sundew,
Bog Pimpernel,   Marsh St John's-wort.

222 **Teucrium scorodonia** Wood Sage *Sàisde Coille*
Frequent on rocky outcrops on hill and on cliffs.

223 **Ajuga reptans** Bugle *Glasair Choille*
Occasional in gullies.

224 **Glechoma hederacea** Ground-ivy *Eidheann Thalmhainn*
Garden weed.

225 **Prunella vulgaris** Selfheal *Dubhan Ceann-chòsach*
Frequent on roadsides and Machair.

226 **★+ Thymus polytrichus subsp. britannicus** Wild Thyme
Lus na Machraidh / Lus an Rìgh
Frequent on rocks, cliffs and Machair.

227 **Mentha arvensis** Corn Mint *Meannt an Arbhair*
Occasional.

228 **Mentha aquatica** Water Mint *Meannt an Uisge*
Frequent in burns and ditches.

229 **Mentha x villosa var alopecuroides** Apple Mint *Meanntas*
Rare.

CALLITRICHACEAE

230 **Callitriche stagnalis** Common Water-starwort
Brailis Uisge / Biolair Ioc
Frequent in peaty pools
Also **C hamulata** Intermediate Water-starwort
Biolair Ioc Meadhanach

PLANTAGINACEAE

231 **Plantago coronopus** Buckshorn Plantain *Adhairc Fèidh*
Frequent on coastal rocks.

232 **Plantago maritima** Sea Plantain *Slàn-lus na Mara*
Frequent on coastal rocks.

233 **Plantago major** Greater Plantain *Cuach Phàdraig*
Frequent on roadsides and waste ground.

234 **Plantago lanceolata** Ribwort Plantain *Slàn-lus*
Frequent on roadsides and grasslands.

235 **Littorella uniflora** Shoreweed *Lus Bòrd an Locha*
At edge of Loch Staonaig.

BUDDLEJACEAE

236 **Buddleja davidii** Butterfly Bush *Preas an Dealain-dè*
Garden escape.

OLEACEAE

237 **Fraxinus excelsior** Ash *Uinnseann*
Near houses.

SCROPHULARIACEAE

238 **Scrophularia nodosa** Common Figwort *Lus nan Cnapan*
Occasional.

239   ★ **Cymbalaria muralis** Ivy-leaved Toadflax *Buabh-lìon Eidheannach*
      On walls in village, near Nunnery.
240   **Digitalis purpurea** Foxglove *Lus nam Ban-sìdh*
      Frequent on hill with bracken.
241   **Veronica serpyllifolia** Thyme-leaved Speedwell *Lus-crè Talmhainn*
      Frequent.
242   **Veronica officinalis** Heath Speedwell *Lus-crè Monaidh*
      Frequent.
243   **Veronica chamaedrys** Germander Speedwell *Nuallach*
      Frequent.
244   **Veronica montana** Wood Speedwell *Lus-crè Coille*
      Rare.
245   **Veronica scutellata** Marsh Speedwell *Lus-crè Lèana*
      Occasional.
246   **Veronica beccabunga** Brooklime *Lochal Mothair*
      Frequent in burns.
247   **Veronica anagallis–aquatica** Blue Water-speedwell *Fualachdar*
      Occasional in burns, only at Calgary on Mull.
248   **Veronica arvensis** Wall Speedwell *Lus-crè Balla*
      Occasional, very small form on Machair.
249   **Veronica agrestis** Green Field-speedwell *Lus-crè Arbhair*
      Rare.
250   **Veronica persica** Common Field-speedwell *Lus-crè Gàrraidh*
      Rare, in fields and gardens.
251   **Veronica filiformis** Slender Speedwell *Lus-crè Claidh*
      Rare, garden weed.
252   **Euphrasia agg** Eyebright *Lus nan Leac*
      Frequent on hill and Machair.
253   **Odontites vernus** Red Bartsia *Modhalan Coitcheann*
      Occasional in grassland and Machair.
254   **Rhinanthus minor** Yellow-rattle *Modhalan Buidhe*
      Frequent in hay fields.
255   **Pedicularis palustris** Marsh Lousewort *Lus Riabhach*
      Occasional in wet parts of hill.
256   ★+ **Pedicularis sylvatica** Lousewort *Lus Riabhach Monaidh*
      Frequent on hill.
LENTIBULARIACEAE
257   ★ **Pinguicula lusitanica** Pale Butterwort *Mòthan Beag Bàn*
      Occasional in bogs, flowers July onwards.
258   ★+ **Pinguicula vulgaris** Common Butterwort *Mòthan*
      Frequent in bogs, flowers May-June.
259   ★ **Utricularia minor** Lesser Bladderwort *Lus nam Balgan Beag*
      Occasional in peaty pools.

CAMPANULACEAE

260 + **Campanula rotundifolia** Scottish Bluebell
Currac-cuthaige/Am Flùran Cluigeanach
Frequent on roadsides and on dry grassland.

RUBIACEAE

261 **Sherardia arvensis** Field Madder *Màdar na Machrach*
Occasional on roadsides and in short grass, very small plants.

262 **Galium palustre** Common Marsh-bedstraw *Màdar Lèana*
Occasional in wet areas.

263 **Galium verum** Lady's Bedstraw *Lus an Leasaich Rùin*
Frequent in dry areas, fields and Machair.

264 **Galium mollugo** Hedge Bedstraw *Màdar Fàil*
Rare.

265 **Galium saxatile** Heath Bedstraw *Màdar Fraoich*
Frequent on hill.

266 **Galium aparine** Cleavers *Garbh-lus*
On shingle and amongst rocks, also garden weed.

CAPRIFOLIACEAE

267 **Sambucus nigra** Elder *Droman*
Occasional, by houses.

268 **Lonicera periclymenum** Honeysuckle *Iadh-shlat/Lus na Meala*
Frequent on cliffs and in gullies.

VALERIANACEAE

269 **Valerianella locusta** Common Cornsalad *Leiteis an Uain*
Occasional, in sandy grass ledges by sea.

270 ⋆ **Centranthus ruber** Red Valerian *Carthan Curaidh Dhearg*
Garden escape in and around Nunnery.

DIPSACEAE

271 **Succisa pratensis** Devil's-bit Scabious *Greim an Diabhail/Ura-bhallach*
Frequent on hill, autumn flowering.

ASTERACEAE [Compositae]

272 **Arctium minus** Lesser Burdock *Cliadan/Leadan Liosda*
Occasional, by farm buildings.

273 **Carduus crispus** Welted Thistle *Fothannan Baltach*
Rare.

274 **Cirsium vulgare** Spear Thistle *Cluaran Deilgneach*
Frequent, arable weed.

275 **Cirsium palustre** Marsh Thistle *Cluaran Lèana*
Frequent.

276 **Cirsium arvense** Creeping Thistle *Fothannan Achaidh*
Frequent, weed of pasture.

277 **Centaurea nigra** Common Knapweed *Cnapan Dubh*
Frequent on field edges.

Machair Plants;
Knotted Pearlwort, Stork's-bill, Milkwort
Bird's-foot-trefoil, Wild Carrot, Wild Thyme.

278 **Cichorium intybus** Chicory *Lus an t-Siùcair*
Rare, probably garden escape.

279 **Lapsana communis** Nipplewort *Duilleag-bhràghad*
Occasional.

280 **Hypochoeris radicata** Cat's-ear *Cluas Cait*
Frequent in grassland.

281 **Leontodon autumnalis** Autumn Hawkbit *Caisearbhan Coitcheann*
Frequent.

282 **Leontodon saxatilis** Lesser Hawkbit *Caisearbhan as Lugha*
Rare.

283 **Sonchus arvensis** Perennial Sow-thistle *Blioch Fochain*
Rare.

284 **Sonchus oleraceus** Smooth Sow-thistle *Bainne Muice*
Occasional in waste places.

285 **Sonchus asper** Prickly Sow-thistle *Searban Muice*
Occasional.

286 **Taraxacum agg** Dandelion *Beàrnan Brìde*
Frequent.

287 **Crepis capillaris** Smooth Hawk's-beard *Lus Curain Mìn*
Frequent, on Machair.

288 **Pilosella officinarum**. Mouse-ear Hawkweed *Srubhan na Muice*
Frequent in short grass.

289 **Hieracium agg** Hawkweeds *Lus na Seabhaig*
Some species present on Iona.

290 **Antennaria dioica** Mountain Everlasting *Spòg Cait*
Frequent on rocky areas on hill and by sea.

291 **Gnaphalium uliginosum** Marsh Cudweed *Cnàmh-lus Lèana*
Rare, in wet fields.

292 **Solidago virgaurea** Golden-rod *Slat Oir*
Frequent in gullies.

293 **Bellis perennis** Daisy *Neòinean*
Frequent and widespread, much on Machair.

294 **Tanacetum parthenium** Feverfew *Meadh Duach*
Rare, garden escape.

295 **Artemisia vulgaris** Mugwort *Liath-lus*
Occasional, on waste ground.

296 **Achillea ptarmica** Sneezewort *Cruaidh-lus*
Frequent on hill.

297 **Achillea millefolium** Yarrow *Eàrr-thalmhainn*
Frequent, in fields and on roadside.

298 **Chrysanthemum segetum** Corn Marigold *Bile Bhuidhe*
Occasional in fields.

299 **Leucanthemum vulgare** Ox-eye Daisy *Neòinean Mòr*
Occasional in fields.

300 **Matricaria discoidea** Pineapple weed *Lus Anainn*
Frequent on rock ledges and cliffs.
301 **Tripleurospermum maritimum** Scentless Mayweed *Buidheag na Mara*
Frequent on rock ledges and cliffs.
302 **Senecio jacobaea** Common Ragwort *Buaghallan*
Frequent, field weed.
303 **Senecio Aquaticus** Marsh Ragwort *Caoibhreachan*
Occasional in wet areas.
304 **Senecio vulgaris** Groundsel *Grunnasg*
Frequent weed.
305 **Tussilago farfara** Colt's-foot *Cluas Liath*
Occasional, early flowering.
306 ★ **Petasites hybridus** Butterbur *Gallan Mòr*
Occasional, early flowering.

JUNCAGINACEAE
307 **Triglochin palustre** Marsh Arrow-grass *Bàrr a' Mhilltich Lèana*
Occasional in wet areas on hill.
308 **Triglochin maritima** Sea Arrow-grass *Bàrr a' Mhilltich Mara*
Occasional, above shore.

POTAMOGETONACEAE
309 **Potamogeton natans** Broad-leaved Pondweed
Liobhag/Duileasg na h-Aibhne
Occasional.
310 **Potamogeton polygonifolius** Bog Pondweed *Liobhag Bhogaich*
Frequent.
311 **Potamogeton berchtoldii** Small Pondweed *Liobhag Bheag*
Rare.

RUPPIACEAE
312 **Ruppia maritima** Beaked Tasselweed *Snàth-lus Mara*
Rare, in brackish pools.

ZOSTERACEAE
313 **Zostera marina** Eelgrass *Bilearach*
In sea, below low water, Sligneach shore.

SPARGANIACEAE
314 **Sparganium angustifolium** Floating Bur-reed *Rìgh-sheisg air Bhog*
Occasional, in peaty pools.

LILIACEAE
315 **Narthecium ossifragum** Bog Asphodel *Bliochan*
Frequent in bogs, flowers August.
316 ★+ **Scilla verna** Spring Squill *Lear-uinnean*
Frequent spring flowering on grassy slopes by sea. Recorded by Lightfoot 1772.
317 ★ **Hyacinthoides non-scripta** Wild Hyacinth, Bluebell
Fuath-mhuc/Bròg na Cuthaig
Frequent, spring flowering in gullies.

Spring Flowers;
Spring Squill, Early-purple Orchid, Dog-violet,
Lesser Celandine,   Primrose.

318   ★ **Allium ursinum**   Ramsons   *Creamh / Gairgean*
        Frequent spring flowering in gullies.
319   **Allium vineale**   Wild Onion   *Gairgean Moire*
        One record 1948, in cliff scrub.

IRIDACEAE
320   ★+ **Iris pseudacorus**   Yellow Iris   *Seileasdair / Sealasdair*
        Frequent and widespread in wet places across island.
321   **Crocosmia x crocosmiflora**   Montbretia
        Garden escape.

ORCHIDACEAE
322   **Gymnadenia conopsea**   Fragrant Orchid   *Lus Taghte*
        Occasional in pasture, flowers July and August.
323   **Coeloglossum viride**   Frog Orchid   *Mogairlean Losgainn*
        Occasional in short turf on sandy soil, plants small, green flowers July and
        August.
324   ★ **Dactylorhiza maculata subsp ericetorum**   Heath   Spotted-orchid
        Mogairlean Mòintich
        Frequent on hill, the most common orchid on Iona, flowers June on.
325   **Dactylorhiza x transiens**
        Rare.
326   **Dactylorhiza x formosa**
        Rare.
327   **Dactylorhiza incarnata subsp. incarnata**   Early Marsh–orchid
        Mogairlean Lèana
        Occasional.
328   **Dactylorhiza purpurella**   Northern Marsh–orchid
        Mogairlean Purpaidh
        Occasional in grass by E shore. Flowers June.
329   ★+ **Orchis mascula**   Early-purple Orchid   *Moth-ùrach*
        Occasional, flowering May-June.

RUSHES, SEDGES and GRASSES

JUNCACEAE
Juncus squarrosus   Heath Rush   *Brù-chorcan / Moran*
Juncus tenuis   Slender Rush   *Luachair Chaol*
Juncus gerardii   Saltmarsh Rush   *Luachair Rèisg Ghoirt*
Juncus bufonius   Toad Rush   *Buabh-luachair*
Juncus articulatus   Jointed Rush   *Lachan nan Damh*
Juncus acutiflorus   Sharp-flowered Rush   *Luachair a' Bhlàth Ghèir*
Juncus maritimus   Sea Rush   *Meithean*
Juncus effusus   Soft Rush   *Luachair Bhog*
Juncus conglomeratus   Compact Rush   *Brodh-bràighe*
Luzula sylvatica   Great Woodrush   *Luachair Coille*

Luzula campestris Field Woodrush *Learman Raoin*
Luzula multiflora Heath Woodrush *Learman Monaidh*
CYPERACEAE
Eriophorum angustifolium Common Cottongrass *Canach*
Eriophorum vaginatum Harestail Cottongrass *Sìoda Monaidh*
Trichophorum cespitosum Deergrass *Cìob/Ultanaich*
Scirpus maritimus Sea Clubrush *Bròbh*
Isolepis setacea Bristle Clubrush *Curcais Chalgach*
Isolepis cernua Slender Clubrush *Curcais Chaol*
Eleogiton fluitans Floating Clubrush *Curcais air Bhog*
Eleocharis quinqueflora Few-flowered Spikerush *Bioran nan Lusan Gann*
Eleocharis multicaulis Many-stalked Spikerush *Bioran Badanach*
Eleocharis palustris Common Spikerush *Bioran Coitcheann*
Eleocharis uniglumis Slender Spikerush *Bioran Caol*
Blysmus rufus Saltmarsh Flatsedge *Seisg Rèidh Ruadh*
Schoenus nigricans Black Bogrush *Sèimhean*
Carex hostiana Tawny Sedge *Seisg Odhar*
Carex binervis Green-ribbed Sedge *Seisg Fhèidh-ghuirm*
Carex viridula Common Yellow Sedge *Seisg Bhuidhe Choitcheann*
Carex extensa Long-bracted Sedge *Seisg Anainn*
Carex rostrata Bottle Sedge *Seisg Shearragach*
Carex pallescens Pale Sedge *Seisg Gheal*
Carex panicea Carnation Sedge *Seisg a' Chruithneachd*
Carex flacca Glaucous Sedge *Seisg Liath-ghorm*
Carex hirta Hairy Sedge *Seisg Ghiobach*
Carex pilulifera Pill Sedge *Seisg Lùbach*
Carex caryophyllea Spring Sedge *Seisg an Earraich*
Carex nigra Common Sedge *Gainnisg*
Carex otrubae False Fox Sedge *Seisg Gharbh Uaine*
Carex arenaria Sand Sedge *Seisg Ghainmhich*
Carex echinata Star Sedge *Seisg Reultach*
Carex ovalis Oval Sedge *Seisg Ughach*
Carex pulicaris Flea Sedge *Seisg na Deargainn*
Carex dioica Dioecious Sedge *Seisg Aon-cheannach*
POACEAE [Gramineae]
Nardus stricta Mat-grass *Riasg*
Festuca pratensis Meadow Fescue *Feisd Lòin*
Festuca arundinacea Tall Fescue *Feisd Ard*
Festuca rubra agg Red Fescue *Feisd Ruadh*
Festuca ovina Sheep's Fescue *Feur-chaorach*
Festuca vivipara Viviparous Fescue *Feur-chaorach Beò-bhreitheach*
Lolium perenne Perennial Rye-grass *Breòillean*
Vulpia bromoides Squirrel-tail Fescue *Feisd Aimrid*
Cynosurus cristatus Crested Dogstail *Coin-fheur*

Puccinellia maritima Common Saltmarsh-grass *Feur Rèisg-ghoirt*
Puccinellia distans Reflexed Saltmarsh-grass *Feur Rèisg-ghoirt Crom*
Poa annua Annual Meadow-grass *Tràthach Bliadhnail*
Poa trivialis Rough Meadow-grass *Tràthach Garbh*
Poa humilis Spreading Meadow-grass *Tràthach Sgaoilte*
Poa pratensis Smooth Meadow-grass *Tràthach an Lòin*
Dactylis glomerata Cocksfoot *Garbh-fheur*
Catabrosa aquatica Whorl-grass *Feur-sùghmhor*
Catapodium marinum Sea Fern-grass *Feur Gainmhich*
Glyceria fluitans Floating Sweet-grass *Mìlsean Uisge*
Helictotrichon pubescens Downy Oat-grass *Feur Coirce*
Arrhenatherum elatius False Oat-grass *Feur Coirce Brèige*
Koeleria macrantha Crested Hair-grass *Cuiseag Dhosach*
Deschampsia cespitosa Tufted Hair-grass *Cuiseag Airgid*
Deschampsia flexuosa Wavy Hair-grass *Mòin-fheur*
Holcus lanatus Yorkshire-fog *Feur a' Chinn Bhàin*
Holcus mollis Creeping Soft-grass *Mìn-fheur*
Aira caryophyllea Silver Hair-grass *Sìdh-fheur*
Aira praecox Early Hair-grass *Cuiseag an Earraich*
Anthoxanthum odoratum Sweet Vernal-grass *Borrach*
Phalaris arundinacea Reed Canary-grass *Cuiseagrach*
Phalaris canariensis Canary-grass *Feur Sìol Eun*
Agrostis capillaris Common Bent *Freothainn*
Agrostis stolonifera Creeping Bent *Fioran*
Agrostis canina Brown Bent *Fioran Mìn*
Ammophila arenaria Marram *Muran* ★
Alopecurus pratensis Meadow Foxtail *Fiteag an Lòin*
Alopecurus geniculatus Marsh Foxtail *Fiteag Cham*
Phleum pratense Timothy *Feur Cait*
Phleum bertolonii Smaller Catstail *Feur Cait Beag*
Phleum arenarium Sand Catstail *Feur Cait Gainmhich*
Bromus racemosus Smooth Brome *Bròmas Mìn*
Bromus hordeaceus Soft Brome *Bròmas Bog*
Anisantha sterilis Barren Brome *Bròmas Aimrid*
Brachypodium sylvaticum False-brome *Bròmas Brèige*
Elytrigia repens Common Couch *Feur a' Phuint*
Elytrigia juncea Sand Couch *Glas-fheur*
Danthonia decumbens Heath-grass *Feur Monaidh*
Molinia caerulea Purple Moor-grass *Fianach*
Phragmites australis Reed *Cuilc / Seasgan*

FERNS and THEIR ALLIES

Selaginella selaginoides Lesser Clubmoss *Garbhag Bheag*
Equisetum fluviatile Water Horsetail *Clois*
Equisetum arvense Field Horsetail *Earball an Eich*
Equisetum sylvaticum Wood Horsetail *Cuiridin Coille*
Equisetum palustre Marsh Horsetail *Cuiridin*
Botrychium lunaria Moonwort *Lus nam Mìos / Luanlus*
Osmunda regalis Royal Fern *Raineach Rìoghail*
Polypodium vulgare Polypody *Clach-raineach*
Pteridium aquilinum Bracken *Raineach Mhòr*
Oreopteris limbosperma Lemon-scented Fern *Raineach an Fhàile*
Phyllitus scolopendrium Hart's Tongue *Teanga an Fhèidh*
Asplenium adiantum-nigrum Black Spleenwort *Raineach Uaine*
Asplenium marinum Sea Spleenwort *Raineach na Mara*
Asplenium trichomanes Maidenhair Spleenwort
   Dubh-chasach / Lus a' Chorrain
Asplenium ruta-muraria Wall-rue *Rù Bhallaidh*
Ceterach officinarum Rustyback *Raineach Ruadh*
Athyrium filix-femina Lady-fern *Raineach Moire*
Gymnocarpium dryopteris Oak Fern *Raineach Fhaidhbhile*
Cystopteris fragilis Brittle Bladder-fern *Frith-raineach*
Polystichum aculeatum Hard Shield-fern *Ibhig Chruaidh*
Dryopteris filix-mas Male-fern *Marc-raineach*
Dryopteris affinis Scaly Male-fern *Mearlag*
Dryopteris aemula Hay-scented Buckler-fern *Raineach Phreasach*
Dryopteris dilatata Broad Buckler-fern *Raineach nan Radan*
Blechnum spicant Hard-fern *Raineach Chruaidh*

ALPHABETICAL INDEX

Numbers refer to Botanical List entries

Scottish Bluebell.

ISLE OF IONA

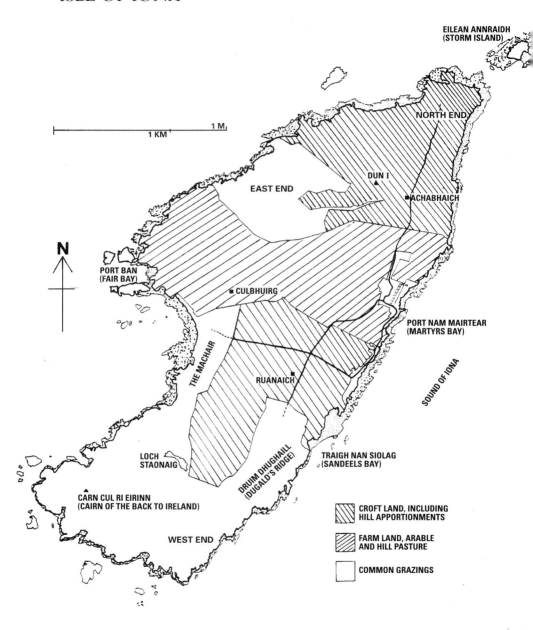

EILEAN ANNRAIDH
(STORM ISLAND)

NORTH END

1 M
1 KM

DUN I ▲

EAST END

ACHABHAICH

N

PORT BAN
(FAIR BAY)

CULBHUIRG ■

PORT NAM MAIRTEAR
(MARTYRS BAY)

THE MACHAIR

RUANAICH ■

SOUND OF IONA

LOCH
STAONAIG

DRUIM DHUGHAILL
(DUGALD'S RIDGE)

TRAIGH NAN SIOLAG
(SANDEELS BAY)

CARN CUL RI EIRINN
(CAIRN OF THE BACK TO IRELAND)

CROFT LAND, INCLUDING
HILL APPORTIONMENTS

FARM LAND, ARABLE
AND HILL PASTURE

COMMON GRAZINGS

WEST END